Joseph and the Coat of Many Colors

(The Coat of Many Colours)

by LAVINIA DERWENT

Pictures by JOE LASKER

American adaptation by Eva Moore

SCHOLASTIC BOOK SERVICES

NEW YORK · TORONTO · LONDON · AUCKLAND · SYDNEY

Adapted from THE COAT OF MANY COLOURS © Lavinia Derwent 1965. This adaptation © Scholastic Magazines, Inc. 1967. This edition is published by Scholastic Book Services, a division of Scholastic Magazines, Inc., by arrangement with Burke Publishing Co. Ltd.

5th printing .... September 1970

Printed in the U.S.A.

Contents

A New Coat for Joseph

"Me! Let me try, Joseph. Let me!"

Joseph was fitting an arrow to a bow. A small boy came running toward him. It was his younger brother, Benjamin.

"Let me try," Benjamin said. He held out his hands to take the bow.

Joseph laughed. His small brother was so eager! Yet Joseph was young enough himself to understand.

"Try if you like," he said. He handed Benjamin the bow. "But it is too heavy for you, Benjamin. Your arms are not strong enough yet."

"Oh yes. They are strong enough," Benjamin said, holding the bow tightly in both hands.

The little boy wanted to copy everything his big brother did. If Joseph could shoot a bow and arrow, so could he.

"There," said Joseph. "Do it like this. Now bend the bow as far as it will go."

Benjamin tried, but the bow really *was* too heavy for him. The arrow fell to the ground only a few feet away.

"O-o-oh," Benjamin let out a cry.

Joseph gave his young brother a pat. "Never mind, Benjamin," he said. "You'll beat me someday. Wait and see."

Benjamin ran to get the arrow. "You shoot it, Joseph! Show me. Make it go as far as that tree." He pointed to a tree that stood a long way off — a thin and old and withered tree. It was not an easy target. But like all boys, Joseph wanted to be a hero to his younger brother.

"I'll try," he said. He fitted an arrow to the bow.

Joseph took aim. He drew the bow back and then let go. *Twang!* Away flew the arrow, straight to the target. It hit the tree and sank into the bark.

"Oh, Joseph!" cried Benjamin.

"You will do as well when you are older," laughed Joseph. "Let's go and get the arrow. I'll show you how to hold the bow . . ."

But just then a voice called, "Joseph! Are you there, my son? Come, I want you."

This was a voice that Joseph always obeyed.

It was his father's voice.

"Coming!" Joseph called. He was always happy to do something to help his father. He put down the bow and arrow, and ran to the house where Jacob, his father, was waiting.

Jacob was smiling when his son entered the house.

"Come here, Joseph," he said. "I have something for you." He held up the most beautiful coat Joseph had ever seen. It was a coat of many colors — red stripes, blue stripes, yellow and green stripes.

Joseph could not believe his eyes. "For *me?*" he asked. He had never had a coat like this before.

"Yes, of course, my son. I made it for you. Put it on."

"Oh thank you, Father, thank you," cried Joseph. "It is beautiful!"

Jacob helped his son put on the coat. "I wanted to give you the most beautiful thing I could think of," he said, beaming with happiness.

Jacob had twelve sons. Ten of them were grown men, too old to play games the way Benjamin and Joseph did. All Jacob's sons helped him on his farm in the land of Canaan, near Jerusalem.

Jacob loved all his sons, but there was one he loved best. And that was Joseph.

Joseph was a young boy, but his father felt he could trust Joseph more than the older sons. He could talk to Joseph about his problems and about his plans. The boy always seemed to understand.

And there was something else that made Joseph different from the others — his dreams.

Jacob, too, had been a dreamer. When he was young, he had seen visions and heard God's voice speaking to him in his sleep. Now Joseph was having the same kind of dreams.

Joseph's older brothers saw that he was their father's favorite, and they were very jealous of him. When Joseph told them about the dreams he had, they became more jealous than ever.

"I had a strange dream last night," Joseph said to his brothers one day. They were working together in the fields.

"Who cares about your dreams?" said his brother Simeon in an angry voice. "No one wants to hear."

"But I dreamed about you and my other brothers," said Joseph. "We were all in the field."

"What's so strange about that?" Simeon said, and he turned away.

"But it was strange," Joseph said. "The stacks of grain came to life."

This made the brothers curious. "The stacks of grain?" they asked, stopping their work.

"Yes," said Joseph. "We were all in the field, tying the grain into stacks. Then, all of a sudden, my stack stood by itself. Your stacks stood around it. And they bowed low before mine. They bowed as if they were bowing to a great ruler."

"A great ruler! You?" the brothers laughed. "What a silly dream."

All the same, the brothers began to wonder.

Could it be that this dream had a hidden meaning? It seemed to show that Joseph stood out above them. What if the dream came true? What if young Joseph was to become the greatest in the family? The very thought made the brothers more jealous.

Joseph had another dream a few nights later. He dreamed that he saw the sun, the moon, and eleven stars all bow down to him. He told his brothers about this dream too.

Eleven stars, the brothers thought. Were these Joseph's eleven brothers?

"Go away!" they shouted at him. "We won't listen to any more silly dreams. Get out of our sight!"

Joseph was sorry his brothers were angry. He wanted his whole family to live together in peace. He did not mean to set himself above the others, but the dreams came to him. He could not stop dreaming, could he?

From now on, Joseph thought, *I'll keep my dreams to myself.*

Joseph tried to keep out of his brothers' way, but now he was too excited about his new coat to keep it a secret. He ran out into the fields, where his brothers were working.

"Look!" he called. "See what Father has given me — a coat of many colors."

The brothers took one look at Joseph and then turned away. They did not say a word to him, but their voices were very angry as they talked to each other.

"Why should we have to wear shabby coats while he dresses like a prince?" one said. "We work harder than he does, but Father never gives us such fine clothes."

"Just look at him, showing off in his fine coat," another said. "Who does he think he is? Does he want us to bow down to him as we did in his dreams?"

"No, no," cried Joseph. "I only wanted to show you my new coat."

"Off with you!" shouted Simeon. "Who wants to see your new coat? Who wants to see you?" And he pushed Joseph away.

Slowly, Joseph walked back to the house. Slowly, he took off his beautiful coat.

What good was having a coat of many colors if his brothers hated him?

"Do not pay attention to them, my son," Jacob said when he heard what had happened. "Wear your new coat. They will soon forget to be so angry."

Joseph Looks for His Brothers

Soon after Joseph got his coat, there was peace at home. His brothers had taken the sheep and goats to feed in a pasture many miles away.

The brothers made this trip every year when the hot, dry weather came, and the land dried up, and there was no grass for the animals to eat.

Every year Joseph begged to go along. What an adventure it would be to camp out, he thought. But the brothers laughed at him. "This

job for men, not for dreamers," they would
ay. "Stay at home and play with your bow and
arrow."

Now the brothers had been gone for many
many days. Jacob began to worry about them.
What if wild animals attacked his sons? What if
robbers broke into the camp?

Joseph saw that his father was worried, and
he guessed the reason.

"Let me go and find my brothers," Joseph
suggested. Here was a chance to prove that he
was as brave as they.

But Jacob did not want Joseph to go. It was
bad enough having his older sons away from
home. How could he let Joseph, his favorite,
out of his sight?

"It will only be for a little while," Joseph
said. "Please. Please, Father, let me go. I can
look after myself."

Jacob could not say no to his favorite son.
"Very well," he said at last. "You may go. And
God go with you."

"Oh, thank you, Father!" cried Joseph. "I will set out at once." And he started to run out of the house.

"Wait, son," Jacob called him back. "You must take some food with you. And remember, watch out for wild animals and for robbers. And Joseph — come back soon."

"Yes, Father, I will come back," Joseph promised.

Jacob helped Joseph put on his coat of many colors. Then, when the boy had put some food in his pocket, he stood at the door and watched till Joseph was out of sight. The reds, blues, greens, and yellows of the coat made a bright splash of color.

One last wave. And Joseph was gone.

In the pasture, Joseph's brothers were sitting around the campfire.

"It's almost time to go home," said one brother. "Father will be pleased when he sees how well we have taken care of the animals."

"Yes," said another. "It will be good to be home again. If only we didn't have to see Joseph!"

"Joseph! Huh!" Simeon said. "I wonder if he has dreamed any more silly dreams. I wonder if he has been given any more fine clothes to wear."

"Who knows what else he has wheedled out of Father," said another brother. "Soon Joseph will be too grand to do any work."

"If only we could get rid of him," they said.

Then Simeon gave a cry. "Look! Someone is coming this way."

The young men jumped up. They put their hands over their eyes and looked out over the pasture. Someone *was* hurrying toward them. Was it someone they knew? The brothers could see the colors of the coat he was wearing — green, red, blue, and yellow.

"It's Joseph!" cried Simeon in anger. "Has he come to show off his fine coat? We don't want him here. Let's send him away."

"Wait," Judah said. He had a sly smile on his

face. "I have a better idea. We wanted to get rid of him. This is our chance."

"But how?" said the others. "Tell us." They stood around Judah.

Judah pointed to a deep pit nearby.

"We will kill Joseph," he said. "And we will throw his body into the pit."

"Yes, yes," said the others. "Then we will be rid of him forever."

"But how can we go home without him?" said one of the brothers. "What can we say to Father?"

"We will say that some wild animals attacked him," Judah answered. "It will be easy."

"No," said Reuben. Reuben did not like what his brothers were saying. He was jealous of Joseph, but he did not hate him as the others did. And he did not want to kill anyone.

"Why should we kill him?" Reuben said. "Throw him into the pit if you must. He will soon starve to death." Reuben had a secret plan. He would come back and get Joseph out of the pit.

"Very well," said the others. There was no time to make other plans.

"Look out," said Judah, "here he comes."

In the Pit

"Reuben! Judah! Simeon!" Joseph called their names when he saw them standing around the campfire. He waved to his brothers as he ran up to them.

"Greetings!" he cried. "How glad I am to see you! You have been gone so long that Father was worried about you. He sent me to find you . . ."

No answer. Instead, the brothers started to move in around Joseph. Their faces were full of hate. Suddenly, they reached out for him. They began to grab at his coat of many colors.

"Off with the coat!" they shouted.

"Throw him into the pit!"

"No, no!" Joseph cried. His brothers were holding him so tightly he could not get away.

"Help!" he called. "Someone help me!" There was no one to hear Joseph — no one but his brothers.

They tore off Joseph's coat and kicked it in the dust. Then they lifted the boy and carried him to the pit.

"Into the pit with him!" they cried. "Into the pit!"

"Please stop," begged Joseph. "Let me go" — but they did not listen. They threw him down into the deep dark pit.

For a long time, Joseph lay still at the bottom of the pit. He was alive, but too stunned to move.

After a while, he heard the voices of his brothers far above him.

"Good. We will never see him again!" said one.

"He will never again show off in his coat of many colors!"

"What good will his dreams do him now?" Simeon sneered.

Joseph stood up and tried to climb the walls of the pit. No use. The walls were smooth and slippery. He could not pull himself up — there was nothing to hold on to.

Joseph called out to his brothers. "Let me out! Let me out, please," he begged. But they only laughed.

"Never!" shouted Judah. "You will stay there until you die!

"Come," he said to the others. "Let's eat our meal in peace." And they all walked away from the pit.

After they had eaten, the brothers got ready to leave. They talked about the tale they would tell their father when they reached home.

"The coat!" cried Judah, picking it up out of the dust. "We can dip it in goat's blood. It will tell its own story. When Father sees it, he will think wild animals have killed Joseph."

"Yes, and he will weep and moan," said

another brother. "But afterward we will have peace . . . and no more favorites."

Just then they heard a sound in the distance.

"Look!" cried Simeon. "Camels — a caravan. The men have seen us. They are coming this way."

As the caravan came closer, the brothers saw that the camels were loaded with rich-smelling spices and costly goods.

"They must be very rich," Judah said. "Perhaps they will buy from us."

"But what have we to sell?" Reuben asked. "Goats?"

Judah smiled wickedly. "Something better than goats," he said. "Something that will bring us much money —" and he pointed to the pit where Joseph was trapped — "a slave!"

From deep in the pit, Joseph could hear strange voices. Had someone come to save him? He cried for help. There was no answer.

Then Joseph heard his brothers talking with the strangers. It sounded as if his brothers were trying to sell something.

"No, no, give us more money." It was Judah's voice. "He is strong and will work hard," Judah went on. "We want more money for this slave."

Slave! Now Joseph understood. His brothers were selling *him* to the strangers. He would be taken far away to a strange country. As a slave, he would be made to work hard. He would go hungry. He would be beaten and whipped. *But I will be alive*, Joseph thought. *Maybe these men will treat me well. Or maybe I will have a chance to run away.*

A minute later, Joseph was pulled out of the pit. He was alive, but he was no longer free. He belonged to the strangers.

Without a word to him, the brothers picked up their packs and walked away.

Only Reuben turned back to look at his young brother. Their eyes met, but what could Reuben say? It was too late. He could not help Joseph now.

Reuben turned away sadly. He went off with the others, carrying the coat of many colors under his arm.

At the farm, Jacob was waiting for his favorite son to come home. Every now and then he would look out, hoping for a sight of Joseph's bright-colored coat. How long every minute seemed when the boy was away!

"Will Joseph be home soon?" Benjamin asked.

"Yes, Benjamin, he will be home soon. Keep watching for him. Tell me if you see him coming."

The little boy ran outside. There was nothing to see but the dry land and the tree that Joseph had hit with an arrow so many weeks ago.

Benjamin stood by the door for a long time. Then he thought he saw something moving in the distance. He rubbed his eyes. Yes, he *did* see something! He saw sheep and goats. He saw men following the animals.

"Joseph is coming!" he called out. "Joseph is coming!"

Jacob heard the little boy and ran outside.

"Come, Benjamin," he said. "We will go and meet him halfway."

The old man hurried as fast as he could while Benjamin skipped on ahead.

Now Jacob could make out the tall figure of Simeon. He could see Reuben and Judah and the others. But it was the smaller figure he wanted to see. Where was Joseph? Was he behind them all, rounding up a stray sheep?

As they came nearer, Jacob saw that Judah was carrying something in his arms. Was it a lamb?

No. It was a bundle of colors — red, green, blue, yellow ... Joseph's coat! And it was splashed with another color — the color of blood!

"My son! My son!" Jacob cried out. "He is dead!"

Sold in the Slave Market

Joseph was alive, but he was far away from his home and his father. He was far away from the land of Canaan. The strangers had taken him to a market place in Egypt. Here men were bought and sold like animals.

Joseph stood with the other slaves in the market place. It was hot and dusty. The noise of dogs barking, men shouting, and whips cracking filled the air.

Joseph was hot and tired and thirsty. His whole body ached. He had walked many miles, with little to drink or eat. And now whips were lashing out from all sides, striking at him. People who came to the slave market thought it was fun to whip the slaves like this and laugh at them.

And the man who was selling Joseph showed no mercy. If the boy started to sink to the ground, the man would pull him up by a rope tied around his waist. And then he would whip Joseph across the shoulders.

One by one the slaves were sold. The crowd cheered as each slave was led away by his new master.

Suddenly there was a stir in the crowd. Everyone watched as a tall man came into the market place. By the way he walked, and the way the people bowed down to him, it was easy to see that he was an important man.

"Make way," the cry went up. "Make way for Potiphar, the captain of the king's guard!"

The great man walked right up to the place where the slaves were being sold. All the men who had slaves to sell wanted Potiphar to buy from them.

"Can I help you, O great Potiphar?" asked one.

"This way, great Captain," said another. "See, I have a fine slave to sell."

But Potiphar did not even look at them. He had already made up his mind.

"This young fellow," he said, and he pointed to Joseph. "Who is selling him?"

"I am, great Captain." Joseph's owner bowed low. "A fine fellow he is, too. Strong as an ox." The man pulled on the rope that bound Joseph. "Stand up straight, boy," he shouted.

It was hard for Joseph to stand straight, but he tried. As he lifted up his chin, he looked right into the eyes of the king's guard. He saw that they were kind eyes.

For the first time since his brothers had thrown him into the pit, Joseph felt hope. If he had to be a slave, he thought that this man would be a kind and fair master. He prayed that Potiphar would buy him.

Potiphar turned to Joseph's owner. "How much?"

Joseph held his breath as the two men argued about a price. His heart beat faster as he waited. Would his owner ask for too much money? Or would Joseph go with the king's guard, the great Potiphar?

Yes! Potiphar took out some money and paid the man. Joseph dropped to his knees in thanks.

"Get up!" shouted the man, and he pulled Joseph to his feet. He handed the rope to Potiphar.

"No — untie him," said Potiphar. Then he turned to speak to Joseph.

"Come," he said. His voice was strong, but not harsh. "Walk beside me."

The people in the market place began to whisper as Joseph and Potiphar left.

"How lucky the boy is to be sold to the king's guard!" they said to each other. "The great Potiphar is a kind man."

"Yes, the boy is lucky," they all agreed.

Joseph raised his head. He was proud to walk beside Potiphar and not be pulled along like other slaves.

"What are you staring at, boy?" Potiphar said to Joseph. "That? It is the king's palace."

Potiphar walked slowly as they came through the gates so that Joseph could look at everything.

Joseph had never seen anything as beautiful as the palace. The walls were painted in bright colors — reds, blues, greens. All around the building were great courtyards. And there were gardens with trees and pools.

"This is the home of the great Pharoah, king of Egypt," Potiphar told Joseph.

The servants who were guarding the palace bowed low to Potiphar, their captain. Joseph saw that even the servants were dressed in rich robes. What, then, must the king be like? Joseph wondered.

It was a long time before Joseph was strong enough to do any work. Potiphar let him rest and saw that he had enough food to eat. As the days went by, Joseph began to feel well again. But every time he saw a bright-colored robe, his heart would sink. The robe reminded him of the coat his father had given him. Then he would think of his father and of all that had happened.

Father must think I am dead. If only I could let him know I'm alive! Does Benjamin miss me? And what of the others — are they sorry for what they have done?

As soon as Joseph was strong enough, Potiphar gave him many jobs to do. Joseph was so busy that he did not have much time to think of his home and his family.

Joseph's one wish was to serve the great captain who had been so kind to him. He was always ready to answer his master's call. He did his work quickly and did not complain.

This pleased Potiphar very much. One day he called Joseph. "Come with me," he said. "I have been watching the way you work, and I see that you can be trusted. I want you to live and work in my house."

This was wonderful news! To work in Potiphar's fine house as a trusted servant! No wonder the other slaves looked at him with envy. He would have the best food to eat and fine robes to wear. He would have more freedom than they had.

"See," the slaves whispered to each other. "The new one — Joseph — is our master's favorite."

"Why should that boy live better than we do?" they sneered.

It was happening all over again. Joseph's troubles began when his father showed that he loved Joseph more than his other sons. Now Potiphar was showing that he liked Joseph more than the other slaves. And the slaves were as jealous as his brothers had been.

Was there more trouble in store for Joseph?

A Promise and a Lie

As time passed, Joseph grew into a handsome young man. He became so helpful to Potiphar that the captain often praised him. "Joseph is worth twenty of the rest," he would say. "What would I do without him?"

But the more Potiphar praised Joseph, the more the other slaves hated him.

"Look at the way the master pats him on the shoulder," one said.

"Just wait," another slave warned. "Someday Joseph will be giving us orders. How will you like that?"

Joseph was too busy to notice the whispering and the jealousy. He was happy, too — except when he thought of his father and Benjamin. But as time went on, he had less time to think about the past. Too much was happening today.

Now that Joseph was a grown man, Potiphar turned to him more and more. Potiphar found that this young slave could understand his problems better than many of his friends who were older. And whenever Joseph had to make a decision on his own, it always seemed to be the right one.

"How glad I am I found you," Potiphar told Joseph. "You take so many worries off my shoulders."

Potiphar's biggest worry, of course, was guarding the king. As captain, he had to train the guards and see that all the king's wishes were obeyed. Added to this, Potiphar had to run his own household. There was food to buy and servants to keep busy. There were a hundred other jobs to be done. And in the household

Joseph helped him more than anyone else.

One day, Potiphar called Joseph to him. "Joseph," he said, "I have made up my mind. You have worked hard and learned quickly. It is time you had a reward. You have proved that you can be trusted. I am going to put you in charge of my household."

Joseph stared at him in surprise. "In charge? You mean that I will give orders?"

"Yes. And you will look after the supplies and the money. You have done it before with my help. Now you will do it yourself. I know you will not fail me."

Joseph felt proud. He stood very straight and looked into his master's eyes. "I will not fail you, great Captain," he promised.

Joseph kept his promise. He ran the household so well that Potiphar was able to spend all his time looking after the king's safety. No wonder the captain was so pleased with him. And Potiphar's wife was pleased, too. She liked having a cheerful young man to talk with.

Joseph used his new power wisely. He never gave a sharp command to the other slaves. He always did his share of the heavy work. And whenever there was a quarrel, he tried to settle it fairly.

But no matter how kind he was to them, the slaves hated him. They began to make up evil stories, hoping to get rid of him. One day, some of the slaves went to see Potiphar. They told him evil stories they had made up.

"That slave Joseph is cheating and stealing," they said. "And something worse than that — he is spending too much time with your wife."

"That can't be true!" Potiphar cried.

"Ask the great lady herself," the wicked slaves said. "She will tell you."

The truth was that Potiphar's wife had come to like Joseph too much. When Joseph saw this, he stayed away from her as much as he could. This made the great lady very angry, and the slaves knew it. They knew she would say anything to get Joseph in trouble — just to get even with him.

"All the stories you have heard about Joseph are true!" Potiphar's wife cried when Potiphar asked her. "You must not trust Joseph any more. He should be put away — into prison!"

And Potiphar believed her. He was so angry that he would not even listen to Joseph.

"You have tricked me!" he shouted at Joseph. "Never will I trust you again!"

"Master, master — what are you saying?" asked Joseph.

But Potiphar turned to the slaves. "Throw him into prison!" he ordered. "Get him out of my sight!"

The slaves were glad to obey. Their plan had worked well. They tied Joseph's hands and feet and dragged him off.

"There!" they shouted when they threw Joseph into the prison. "See what happens to the captain's favorite! You will never get out of here alive!"

Prison

Joseph lay on the floor of the prison. He could not move. It was dark — as dark as the pit where his brothers had thrown him so many years before. The thought that Potiphar no longer trusted him or believed in him made Joseph's heart ache.

Then the words of the slaves came back to Joseph: "You will never get out of here alive. Never!" Was there no hope?

As he lay in the prison, Joseph remembered the God his father prayed to. Surely God had not turned away from him. In the dark of the cell,

Joseph began to pray. He asked God to help him and give him courage.

"Come, it is not so bad."

Joseph lifted his head. Had someone spoken?

Yes. It was the old jail keeper.

"It is not so bad," the old man said again. "Here, let me untie these ropes. Then you will be able to move about."

Suddenly Joseph had a feeling of hope. In this dark prison, he had found a friend.

Joseph was not alone in the prison. Many other men were crowded together in the small room. Some of them were chained. Others just sat in the corners with their heads bowed.

No one thought of helping the jail keeper with his many jobs — no one but Joseph. Instead of sitting around, grumbling and complaining, Joseph helped to sweep and clean the floor of the cell. He held the pot while the jail keeper dished out the small helpings of food to the prisoners.

The old man was glad to have a willing helper.

"I will give you a special job," he said to Joseph one day. "I will put you in charge of the new prisoners."

From then on, Joseph had so much to do that he was always busy. The days seemed shorter. Still, he longed to be free. He longed to breathe fresh air again and feel the sun on his face.

Most of all, Joseph wished for a chance to talk to Potiphar and tell his master that he had not failed him.

At night, Joseph dreamed strange dreams. He was back at home with his father and brothers, working on the farm and wearing his coat of many colors. But in the morning he would awake to find himself in prison and the door still shut. Would it ever open and set him free?

The Butler and the Baker

One day there was a loud knock at the prison door.

"More visitors," said the old jail keeper. "We are too crowded already. Oh well — I will leave them in your care, Joseph."

The door creaked open and two men were thrown into the room.

"Look!" the other prisoners whispered to each other. "That's the king's butler, who waits at his table!"

"And that's his baker, who makes his bread and cakes!"

"The king must be very angry with them to have them put into prison."

The two men turned their backs on the others and would not speak. They kept to themselves. Joseph could do nothing to help them.

One night, many weeks later, the butler and baker were sleeping restlessly. They tossed and turned on the hard floor. And in the morning they whispered together, as if telling each other secrets. But they would not speak to anyone else.

When Joseph came to give them their share of food, he saw that the men were looking very worried.

"Is something the matter?" he asked. "Is there anything I can do to help?"

The men looked at each other and shook their heads. "No, no," said the baker. "It is only our dreams."

"Dreams?" said Joseph. He sat down beside them. "I, too, am a dreamer," he said. "Dreams have strange meanings. Perhaps I can tell the meaning of yours."

The men turned away from Joseph and whispered together some more. Then, suddenly, they made up their minds. They would speak.

The butler told his dream first.

"I dreamed of a vine with three branches full of grapes," he said. "I took the grapes and squeezed the juice into the king's cup. Then I put the cup into his hand. What can it mean?"

"I know! It is good news!" cried Joseph. "The three branches of grapes mean three days. In three days the king will send for you. In your dream, he took the cup from you. That means he will take you back into his household. Wait and see. In three days you will be free."

The butler smiled. "Good news indeed! If only it will come true."

"It will come true," Joseph promised. Then he turned to the baker. "Now tell me your dream."

The baker had a strange dream too.

"In my dream, I had three white baskets on my head, one on top of the other. The baskets were full of bread and cakes for the king. But suddenly some great birds swooped down and ate the food from the top basket. What can it mean?"

The baker looked at Joseph, waiting to hear some good news. But this time Joseph shook his head. The dream was not good. In three days the prison door would open for the baker too, but he would not be set free. He would be put to death.

The baker did not believe Joseph. "It is only a dream," he said in an angry voice. "Who believes such silly stories. Go away! Do not speak to me again!"

Three days later the king held a great feast to celebrate his birthday.

"I must have my butler to serve the wine," the king said to his servants. "Send for him. Set him free."

The prison door was opened and the butler was called. "The dream has come true!" he cried, and turned to Joseph. "Is there anything

I can do for you, now that I am free?"

"Tell the king that I have been put into prison unfairly," said Joseph. "Ask him to give me a chance to defend myself."

"Yes, yes," promised the butler, hurrying out of the door. "I will remember."

No sooner was the prison door shut behind the butler than there was another loud knock. The baker turned pale and trembled with fear. The butler's dream had come true, just as Joseph said it would. Now it was his turn . . .

Pharaoh's Dream

Joseph waited for the butler to send someone to free him. But days passed and no one came. Once the butler was back in the palace, he forgot about Joseph. He forgot his promise.

Two years went by.

Then one night, Pharaoh had a strange dream. Could it have a meaning? He sent for the royal magician. If the dream did mean something, perhaps the royal magician could tell him.

The magician listened as Pharaoh told about his dream: "I saw seven fat cows feeding in a meadow near the river," said Pharaoh. "Seven thin cows came up out of the water and attacked the fat cows, and ate them all. Then I woke up."

The magician shook his head. "That is a strange dream indeed," he said.

"But there is more," Pharaoh went on. "After I had fallen asleep again, I had another dream. I saw a stalk of grain. There were seven full, ripe ears growing on it. Then another stalk of grain with seven thin, dry ears came up. It ate the stalk with the full ears. What can it mean?"

He waited for the royal magician to answer. But the magician just shook his head. "They are just dreams, great King. There is no hidden meaning."

But Pharaoh was not sure. "Send for the wise men," he ordered.

The wise men had studied the stars. They knew everything there was to know on earth — but they could not tell Pharaoh what his dreams meant.

"I know these dreams mean something important," Pharaoh said to his butler one day. "The magician can't tell me. The wise men can't tell me. Who could know the answer?"

Then the butler remembered Joseph. For the first time since he was set free from the prison, he remembered his promise. He felt ashamed that he had not kept his word.

"I know, master," he said to Pharaoh. "There is a young man in prison. His name is Joseph. He told me the meaning of a dream I had once. Perhaps he can tell you the meaning of your dreams."

"Send for him!" cried Pharaoh. "Bring him to me at once!"

Joseph was sweeping the dusty floor of the prison when he heard a loud knock on the door. "Open in the name of the king!"

The old jail keeper shuffled to the door. "Another new prisoner!" he grumbled. But there was no prisoner. Two men from the king's guard stood outside.

"We have come for the prisoner, Joseph. The king wants to see him at once."

Joseph let his broom fall to the floor. The king! Why should the great Pharaoh of Egypt want to see him?

Joseph hardly had time to wash and change his robe. Then the guards took him by the arms and hurried him outside.

Joseph blinked his eyes in the bright sun. How wonderful to be out in the fresh air again! If only he could walk slowly through the courtyard. But the guards were in a hurry.

Soon Joseph was in the palace. Two slaves opened the door leading to the king's court. And there was the great Pharaoh himself. He sat on a throne at the end of the room with his wise men around him. Slaves were waving big fans to cool the air.

The guards let go of Joseph and bowed to Pharaoh. Then they pushed Joseph forward. He looked up into Pharaoh's dark face.

"I am told you know the meaning of dreams," Pharaoh said to him. "Come here, Joseph, and listen to mine."

Joseph stood and listened carefully. His eyes never left Pharaoh's face.

When he had told the whole dream, Pharaoh looked straight into Joseph's eyes. "Come, tell me — what is the answer?"

"The answer comes from God and not from me, great King," Joseph said. "It is He who has given me the power to tell the meaning of your dreams."

"And what does God tell you?" asked Pharaoh, leaning forward to listen.

"The seven fat cows mean seven good years for the whole land," Joseph told him. "The cattle will be fat. The crops will be good. It will be a time of plenty."

"Good! Good!" Pharaoh said, and nodded his head.

"But there is more," Joseph said. "After the seven good years, there will be seven years of famine. The cattle will grow thin and die. The grain will be too poor to eat. The people will starve."

The king was silent for a moment. He felt that Joseph was telling the truth. God had sent the dreams as a warning. Perhaps God had also sent this young man Joseph to save the country.

"Is there nothing I can do to stop this famine from coming?" Pharaoh asked him.

"You must find the wisest man in the kingdom. You must make him governor of the whole land of Egypt. During the seven good years, he will see that all the food that is not needed is stored in great barns. Then, when the seven bad years come, he can divide the food among the people. Then no one will starve to death."

It was a simple answer. The king nodded his head again. Here was a wise young man — wiser even than the royal magician and the wise men who stood around his throne.

Suddenly the king knew what he must do. To the surprise of everyone in the court, he took off his ring. He called Joseph to him.

"Give me your hand, Joseph," he said. "Let me place my ring on your finger. It means that you are to be the new governor of Egypt. You are the wisest man in my kingdom!"

Governor of Egypt

"A race! Make way for the chariots!" A cry went up in the busy market place. People stood on tiptoe to watch. They could hear the chariots coming, but all they could see was a cloud of dust. Who was winning the race?

Then the dust rolled away. The racers were coming into sight — they were neck and neck!

One of the chariots was being driven by a strong, proud-looking man — Potiphar, captain of the king's guard. Racing along by his side, wheel to wheel, was a slim young man wearing a robe of many colors — Joseph, governor of Egypt.

The people in the market place waved them on

with a cheer, not really caring who would win. It was the race that mattered.

"Look at the way they drive!" the people exclaimed. "They handle their chariots with great skill."

As the two men came near the gates of the palace, they tugged at the horses' reins and slowed down.

"Well done, Joseph!" cried Potiphar. "You have kept up the pace. A little longer, and you might have beaten me."

"It was you who taught me, Captain," Joseph said. "Thank you for a fine race."

Together they entered the palace gates, side by side — captain and governor.

Many wonderful things had happened to Joseph. But best of all, he and Potiphar were friends again.

At last the slaves had admitted their lies. So had Potiphar's wife. The captain begged Joseph to forgive him. "What can I do to make it up to you?" he asked.

There was only one thing Joseph wanted.

"You can be my friend," he said.

From then on, Joseph and Potiphar were close friends. Joseph often turned to the captain when he had a problem; and the captain often asked his young friend's advice, too. And when they weren't working, they spent much of their time together enjoying sports. Chariot racing was their favorite sport.

Now they left their chariots in the courtyard and walked together to the palace. At the door, the men turned to look out over the land.

"The barns will soon be finished," Joseph said.

Potiphar nodded. In the distance he could see men building great barns where grain would be stored.

"Do you really believe it, Joseph?" asked Potiphar. "Even in this time of plenty, there is danger of famine?"

"Yes," answered Joseph. "Great danger. God has given us a warning. We must be ready when the time comes."

And Joseph had wasted no time in getting to work. As the new governor, he ordered all the people of Egypt to build great barns. He told them that no feasts should be held — no food should be wasted. They must save now for the bad years. Even the smallest grain was to be gathered in.

Some people grumbled. "Why should we listen to the governor?" they said. "It is our grain. We have worked hard in the fields. We should be able to do what we want."

Others, however, were ready to follow Joseph's advice. "The great Pharaoh trusts him, doesn't he?" they said. "We should listen to him, too."

The king himself spoke to the people.

"You must obey your new governor," he said. "All that he is doing is for your own good. Do as he says, and the country will be saved."

Some people still complained, but they did as they were told. Soon great barns could be seen all over the land.

Although Joseph grew to love this great country, he never forgot the land of Canaan where he had been born. He always wore robes

made of bright colored cloth. They reminded
him of the coat his father had given him when
he was a boy.

Is Father still alive? Joseph wondered whenever he thought of his family. *Who has taught
Benjamin how to shoot a bow and arrow? And
the others — what are they doing? Will I ever
see them again?*

The years of plenty went by.

One day Potiphar and Joseph were walking
together in the palace yard. Potiphar looked up
at the sky. "Has the wind changed?" he asked.
"There is a strange feeling in the air."

Joseph, too, felt a change. Suddenly he
realized what is was.

"The seven good years are over," he said in
a quiet voice. "The seven years of famine are
coming."

Joseph knew the people of Egypt had nothing
to fear. The barns were full of food — no one in
Egypt would starve.

But far away, in the land where Joseph had
been born, the people were not so lucky.

A Long Journey

In the land of Canaan, a boy stood in the doorway of his father's house. A bow and arrow lay at his feet.

Benjamin was big enough now to shoot the arrow into a far target — just as Joseph had done when Benjamin was a little boy.

But today Benjamin did not feel strong enough to shoot his bow and arrow. He was hungry. For weeks there had been little to eat. All the fields in the land had dried up. No crops would grow. A great famine had come.

"Benjamin . . . " The soft voice of his father called to him.

Jacob did not like to let Benjamin out of his sight. The boy had become as dear to him as Joseph had once been.

Benjamin turned and went inside. "Here I am, Father," he said. "Is there any news?"

"News? What news could there be?" said Jacob. "Things are getting worse every day. Our barns are empty. Our fields are bare. Our cattle are dying."

Benjamin came and sat at his father's feet. He

tried to cheer him. "Perhaps tomorrow the weather will change. Perhaps rain will come . . ."

Jacob shook his head. "It is too late. If only we had saved some food when we had some to spare! If only we had a wise ruler like the governor of Egypt. I have heard that he told the people to store food. Now they have enough to eat and more to spare."

Benjamin sat up. "Food to spare!" he cried. "Do you think they might sell some? Let me go with my brothers and ask the governor if we may buy some grain."

"To Egypt? Let you go to Egypt? Oh no, my son."

Jacob's eyes filled with tears as he remembered the day he had let Joseph go. His favorite son had never returned. It must not happen again. "You must not leave me," he cried out, holding Benjamin close.

Benjamin understood. He too remembered the day his brothers had brought back a coat stained with blood — Joseph's coat. They said that Joseph had been killed by wild animals. That was many years ago, but Benjamin had never forgotten his brother.

"Then let the others go," Benjamin suggested. "Give them some money. Tell them to buy enough food to keep us from starving."

Jacob looked at his son — he could see that the boy had become thin and pale. He knew they would all die unless something was done quickly.

"Call your brothers, Benjamin," he said. "Tell them to get ready for a long journey."

The ten brothers were on their way to Egypt. Jacob watched them until they were out of sight, just as he had watched Joseph leave so many years before. Then he turned back and went sadly into the house, looking old and lonely. There was no one left now except Benjamin.

Each of the brothers had a donkey with him. Over each donkey's back was an empty sack.

"Let's hope that our load will be heavier on the way home," said Simeon.

"How could the governor send us away empty-handed?" Judah said. "Especially when he sees how much money we have brought." He jingled the coins he carried in a purse.

It was true that they had plenty of money. Jacob had become rich during the good years before the famine. But what use was money in Canaan now? They could not eat money. It was food they needed.

The road to Egypt took the brothers past a familiar spot. This was the same pasture they had gone to every year, bringing the sheep and goats to feed. Now the pasture was as dry and bare as their own farmland. They could see the deep pit where they had thrown Joseph. Even Judah could not pass it without feeling guilty.

Reuben stopped and wiped his forehead. "Do you remember . . . ?" he began. But Judah would not listen.

"That was long ago," he said in a gruff voice. "What good is it to think of the past? We have enough to worry about now. Let's move on."

But as they marched along, each brother was thinking of the boy in the coat of many colors. Had the famine come to punish them for their wicked deed?

The brothers still had many miles to go before they would reach Egypt. Sometimes they walked along dusty roads; sometimes they rode on the backs of their donkeys. The men had so little food to eat that they were very tired. The journey seemed endless. Would they ever reach Egypt?

After many days, the brothers noticed a change in the land around them. The fields along the way were still dry and empty, but the cattle were fat. They looked as if they had been feeding on green grass. And everyone the brothers met looked healthy and well fed. They had come to the land of Egypt at last.

"Look!" cried Reuben, and he pointed to some great buildings. "Those must be the barns where food is stored. See how many there are."

"There should be plenty of food to spare for us," Judah said, hurrying on. "Come! We are nearing the town."

A Strange Meeting

The young governor was busy at work inside the palace. Joseph was now in charge of giving out grain to the people of Egypt. He had also set some aside to sell to anyone from another country who came asking for food.

A sudden sound from the courtyard made Joseph look up from his work. Voices. And one voice — deeper than the others — made Joseph think of the past. Surely this was the voice of his brother Judah!

For a moment, Joseph felt afraid — as afraid as he had been when he last heard that voice, from deep inside a pit. Then joy at the thought of seeing his brother overcame all his other feelings.

Joseph rushed to the window. Yes, it was Judah! And the rest of his brothers were with him — all except Benjamin.

Joseph stepped back to keep out of their sight. Could this be one of his dreams? Or was it really happening? He longed to rush out into the courtyard, but he held back. He must wait. He must find out why they had come to Egypt.

Again he heard Judah's voice, speaking more softly than usual.

"We wish to speak with the governor," he told the palace guard. "We have come to beg some grain."

Beg! That was a strange word for Judah to use. Joseph remembered how he had begged to be let out of the pit, and how Judah had turned away from him. Here was a chance to turn Judah away, but was that what he wanted to do?

The guard came in. "Strangers have asked to

see you, master," he said, bowing low. "They are begging for grain."

"Send them in," he said, trying to keep his voice steady. Then a sudden idea came to him. "Wait! I must change my robe."

Joseph did not want his brothers to see him dressed in a bright-colored robe. He did not want them to guess who he was. Not yet.

"Bring me a plain robe," he ordered a slave. "Bring my rings and my gold chain."

When the brothers came in, they saw the young governor standing in the shadows. Rings sparkled on his fingers and gold glittered from

the chain around his
neck. The robe he wore
was made of the finest
cloth they had ever seen.

The ten brothers fell
to their knees and bowed
down before him. And
as they did so, Joseph
remembered his dream
when his brothers' stacks
of grain had bowed to
his stack. The dream was
coming true!

Joseph tried to control his feelings. He wanted to throw his arms around his brothers and forgive them. Yet he must make sure of one thing first. He must know that they were sorry for the wicked deed they had done.

"You may stand," he said. "Let me know who you are. Where have you come from, and what do you want?'"

The brothers shuffled to their feet and stood before him. Not one of them guessed who Joseph really was. Then Judah stepped forward to speak.

"We have come a long way, master, from the land of Canaan. Our fields have gone dry and our family is dying of hunger. We are here to beg for some grain."

"To beg?" said Joseph in a surprised voice.

"To buy!" said Judah, quickly pulling out some silver coins. "Look, master, we have plenty of money. We will pay any price you ask."

"Wait! — not so fast. There are many things I must know first."

"What things, master?" asked Judah. He was

ready to please this great man in any way he could.

"Tell me," said Joseph, pointing to the others. "Who are these men?"

"They are my brothers, who have come with me. We all work together on our father's farm."

"Ten brothers in the family?" asked Joseph.

"No master. Eleven," Judah answered slowly. "Our youngest brother, Benjamin, is at home with my father."

Joseph turned away to hide the joy he felt. This is what he wanted to hear — his father and Benjamin were both alive and well.

"So — you are eleven brothers?" he said, turning back to face them. "Is that all in the family?"

Judah did not speak. Instead, Reuben stepped out and answered the question. "We were twelve, master."

"Twelve brothers, then? Where is the missing one?" asked the governor of Egypt.

All the brothers looked down at the floor as

Judah spoke.

"He is no longer with us," he said. Then, trying to change the subject, he went on. "Master, how much grain can you spare us?"

"Wait. I want to know a great deal more about your family before I decide. You say your brother is no longer with you?"

Judah did not answer right away. This was something he did not want to talk about. "We do not know where he is, master," he answered at last.

"A strange family, indeed!" said Joseph. "How do I know that your story is true? You might have come to spy on Egypt to see how much grain we have."

"No, no," Judah said. "Our story is true. We have come to buy only enough grain to feed our family."

"Then why didn't you bring your youngest brother with you?" asked Joseph, still pretending he didn't believe them.

"Our father could not part with him. Our father is an old man . . ."

"And now that he has lost one son, he is afraid to lose another?" said Joseph, looking straight into Judah's eyes.

Judah looked down. It seemed as if this young governor knew their secret and was trying to make them confess.

"It was a long time ago," Judah said in a low voice.

"So long ago that you have forgotten your brother? Or do you remember his name?"

"His name was Joseph," Reuben spoke up. "No, master, we have not forgotten our brother. Many times we wish . . ."

"What do you wish?"

But Judah broke in. "Please, master, will you let us buy some grain? We have come a long way and are eager to get home again."

Joseph nodded his head. "Yes, you may buy as much grain as you want — on one condition."

"What is it?" the brothers asked. "We will do anything you ask."

"You must prove that your story is true." Joseph drew a deep breath. "Go back to Canaan and bring Benjamin, your youngest brother, to me."

The brothers turned pale. This was the one thing they could *not* do.

"No," Reuben said. "Our father would never let the boy go."

"Then I must believe you are spies!" Joseph said, and his voice was cold. "Guards!" he called "Take these spies. Put them into prison."

Joseph Makes a Bargain

For three days the brothers sat in the dark prison. They were all wondering the same thing: were they being punished now for selling Joseph as a slave? Their hearts were filled with regret. And they were worried.

"What shall we do?" they asked one another. "Father and Benjamin will soon starve if we don't come with food."

"We must bring Benjamin back," Judah said. "It is the only way."

On the third day,
Joseph came to see them.

"We will do as you ask,
master," said Judah. "Let us buy
some grain, and we will bring our
youngest brother to you. You will see that we
are telling the truth."

But Joseph wanted to be sure they would keep their promise. "All right," he said. "I will set you free. But one of you must stay here as a hostage. You!" Joseph pointed to Simeon. "You will stay here until your brothers come back."

Many days later, the nine brothers were nearing home. It had been a slow journey, for their sacks were heavy with grain. The donkeys could hardly carry these heavy loads.

The animals were so thin that their bones almost showed through their skin. They had been well fed at the palace, but that was a long time ago.

"Let's stop and give the donkeys something to eat," said Judah, untying his sack.

But when he opened the sack, his face suddenly went pale. He gave a cry.

"What is it? What has happened?" said his brothers, running to him. One look at the sack, and they too grew pale with fear.

"The money we paid for the grain!" cried Judah. "Look! It is lying in the top of the sack.

How did it get there? The governor will think we have stolen it!"

"We are surely being punished," Reuben cried. "The governor has guessed our secret. And now he will say that we have robbed him. What shall we do?"

Judah closed the sack. "Let us hurry home. What else can we do? We cannot turn back now."

So they went on, feeling more unhappy than ever. They did not guess that Joseph himself had put the money in the sack. If they were honest, thought Joseph, they would bring the money back.

"They are coming! I can see them, far away!" Once more, Benjamin was at the door, watching and waiting for his brothers to return.

Jacob hurried out when he heard his son's shouts. Both he and Benjamin were thin and weak from hunger.

"Can you see?" Jacob asked. "Are the sacks full?"

"Yes! Yes, I can see. They are all full!"

Jacob gave a thankful sigh. "Well done, my sons!" he cried. Then he turned to Benjamin. "We will go and meet them."

As Jacob walked forward, a sudden fear filled his heart. He was thinking about that other time he had gone to meet his sons, only to find that one was missing.

"See," Benjamin was saying. "Reuben is waving to us! . . . and there is Judah." Forgetting his weakness, he ran forward, waving and calling, "Welcome home! Welcome home!"

But Jacob had begun to count,". . . six, seven, eight, nine . . ." His heart missed a beat. Where was the tenth?

"Oh no, no," he cried. "One of them is missing!"

At first Jacob could not understand what had happened. Again and again he asked his sons, "Where is Simeon? What has happened?"

Over and over again, the brothers told their story. "The governor of Egypt is a strange man. He is keeping Simeon there until we return. He will give us anything we want — only we must bring Benjamin with us."

"No!" Jacob shook his head. "Never. Benjamin will not go."

But after a while, all the food the brothers had brought from Egypt was gone. Benjamin himself begged his father to let him go.

"It is our only hope, Father," he said. "There is nothing to eat here, but in Egypt there is plenty. Should the whole family starve because of me?"

For a long time, Jacob would not listen. Then at last he gave in. What else could he do?

"If you must go, God go with you, my son," he said to Benjamin. "But if you do not return, my heart will surely break."

"Do not be afraid, Father," Benjamin said. "I will come back."

Jacob told his sons to fill their sacks with silver and other presents for the governor. They must also take back the money they had found in the sack of grain.

The brothers took what food they could find

and were ready to start. This time Jacob did not come to the door to watch his sons leave. Benjamin said good-bye to his father and left the old man sitting alone in the house.

"Don't worry, Father, I will be back soon," the boy said. Then he turned and ran after his brothers.

The Coming of Benjamin

They were nearing the palace gates. Benjamin stared with wide eyes at the beautiful building and the gardens around it. He followed his brothers into the courtyard. At the palace door, they were stopped by a guard.

"What is your business here?"

"We have come to speak with the governor. We want to buy some grain," Judah told the guard.

Inside the palace, Joseph heard Judah's deep

voice — his brothers had come back! Was Benjamin with them? He almost rushed out to see. But he was not yet ready to let his brothers know who he was.

When the brothers came in, they saw the governor dressed in the same fine robe and wearing the same gold chain and sparkling rings.

Joseph's heart beat fast when he saw that Benjamin *was* with them. Without thinking, he took a step toward the boy and held his arms out as if he were going to hug him. Then, suddenly, he stopped and moved away.

"So, you have come back," he said to the brothers in a harsh voice. "And this is your youngest brother?"

"Yes, this is Benjamin," Judah said, and he pushed the boy forward.

Benjamin looked up into the governor's eyes. These eyes reminded him of someone...someone he had once known. But who?

The governor spoke to him in a gentle voice. "Your father? Is he well?"

"Yes, master," Benjamin answered. "He is well. But he is very lonely. He is afraid we will not return."

"Then you must not keep him waiting." Joseph turned to speak to the others. "So, you have come to buy more grain?"

"Yes, master," Judah said. "We have also come to return the money we found in a sack of grain when we were going home."

Joseph almost smiled — he was pleased that his brothers were honest enough to bring back the money. But he pretended to be angry . . . "The money you stole, you mean!" he said in a loud voice.

"We did not steal it, master," Judah said. "Look — here it is. And here are some gifts sent by my father."

Gifts! Joseph's eyes filled with tears. He turned away so that the brothers would not see. Gifts from his father to the governor of Egypt! If only he could thank Jacob in person.

"Send for Simeon!" Joseph said to a slave. "Let

him out of the prison."

Then he said to the brothers, "You must be hungry and tired after your long journey. My servants will prepare a big meal for you to eat before you leave."

The brothers were glad that the governor finally believed them. And they were glad to see Simeon again. Before long, all of them sat down to a great meal.

Joseph told the servants to see that Benjamin got the best food. And he gave the boy his own silver cup to drink from.

"Enjoy your meal," Joseph said to the brothers. "I will order your sacks to be filled with food. Farewell, and have a good journey home." Once again, his eyes rested on Benjamin. Then Joseph left the room.

I've seen him before, thought Benjamin. *But where? Was it in a dream?*

"Stop! Stop! Robbers!"

The ten brothers had just begun the trip home

when they heard these shouts behind them. Men came running after them — men from the king's guard.

"What is this?" cried Judah. "What do you mean? Why are you calling us robbers?"

"Those sacks!" the men said. "Open them at once. They are full of stolen goods."

"No, no," Reuben said. "They are full of grain and food which we have paid for. There is nothing else in them. We have stolen nothing."

But the guards pushed him aside. "We will soon see." They pointed at the sack that was on Benjamin's donkey. "Open it!" they ordered the boy.

Benjamin's fingers were shaking as he undid the rope. And when he saw what was inside, his whole body began to tremble with fear.

"The silver cup!" he cried. "The one I was drinking from. How did it get here?"

"We know!" the guards said. "You stole it. Open those other sacks. See what else has been taken."

One by one, each of the brothers had to open his sack. One by one, each brother let out a cry when he saw what was inside. In every sack was a pile of money — the price they had paid for the grain!

"Come with us, robbers!" ordered the guards. "We will see what the governor has to say about this."

Joseph was waiting for them inside the palace. It was all happening the way he had planned.

His brothers threw themselves down in front of him. They did not dare to look at him.

"Mercy, mercy, master!" they cried. "Show us mercy. We have stolen nothing."

Joseph once again thought of a dream he had once dreamed . . . eleven stars bowing down to him — his eleven brothers. Now that dream was coming true.

"Mercy, show us mercy! Have pity on us!" begged Judah.

Joseph spoke to him in a quiet voice. "Pity? What pity did you show me when I begged for mercy that day you threw me into the pit?"

Slowly the brothers raised their heads. Their eyes opened wide at what they saw. The governor was no longer wearing a plain robe and sparkling jewels. He stood before them dressed in a coat of many colors — red stripes, blue stripes, yellow and green stripes.

"Joseph!" said Reuben in a whisper. "It is our brother Joseph!"

Benjamin jumped to his feet. "Joseph, it is you! You are not dead!" The boy ran into Joseph's open arms.

The other brothers were still kneeling at Joseph's feet. "Forgive us. We are deeply ashamed of what we did. Please forgive us."

The brothers trembled. What would Joseph do? He had the power to punish them in any way he wanted. He could even put them to death. But when they looked up, he was smiling.

"Do not be afraid," Joseph said, holding out his hands to them. "Let us forget the past. You are my brothers, and I am happy to have you with me again. Welcome! Welcome!"

The brothers hugged Joseph, and a great happiness filled their hearts. After all these years, the terrible feeling of shame and guilt was gone.

A Happy Ending

The story of Joseph's brothers soon spread through the palace. When the king heard the story, he sent for his young governor.

"It is a happy time for you, Joseph," Pharaoh said. "And a happy time for the people of Egypt. We have no fear of starving for the rest of the famine. You have done your job wisely."

"I am proud to serve you, great King," Joseph said, bowing low.

"And you have served me well. But how shall I repay you?"

"There is just one thing that would make me

happier than I am now," said Joseph. "That would be to have my brothers and my father here with me forever."

"Then you shall have it! Prepare a place for them," Pharaoh said. "Choose a home with plenty of land for sheep and cattle. Your family can start a new life here."

Everything was made ready. The new house was clean and bright. A great feast was being prepared. And now Joseph was waiting . . . waiting for his brothers to return with Jacob. How long every moment seemed until he would see his father again!

And what of Jacob? How did he feel about leaving his home and traveling to a strange land? Many other men his age would have been afraid to leave everything behind and start a new life. But there was only one thought in Jacob's mind. His son was alive. He would travel a hundred times as far to meet him.

Jacob seemed like a young man again. Younger even than his sons. "Hurry!" he would say to them. "Joseph will be waiting for us."

It was Jacob who led the way through the crowded market place. It was he who first saw the Pharaoh's palace in the distance. It was he who called out, "Look! There is someone waving to us — someone in a coat of many colors. It is Joseph! My son Joseph!"

Joseph was coming to meet his father. The reds, blues, yellows, and greens of his coat flashed in the sunshine. Nearer and nearer. And now at last Joseph was there — no longer a ruler of a great land. He was a boy in a coat of many colors, held close in his father's arms.